This Journal Belongs To:

_____

Hello beautiful soul

First of all, I want to say a huge thank you for purchasing this journal, not only to help support me, but to help support **YOU**. This is a step in your self love journey to begin *implementing self care* into your daily routine.

Hi, I'm Mickeeley, a small town mama + wife that is obsessed with all things *self love + self care*. I'm a Certified Aromatherapist, a wondering soul, and my favorite color is without a doubt always going to be purple.

I own So Posh Soap & Candle Company which was born out my passion for self care. It is my personal mission in life to encourage and *empower women across the country* to develop a daily self care practice.

Self care has drastically changed my life and *I know it can do the same for you too*. Filling your cup every day will allow you to be able to pour into others more without draining yourself.

As you get ready to use this guided journal daily, just remember that self care doesn't have to be an elaborate, expensive thing. It can be as simple as cleaning a junk drawer, calling a friend, or just going to bed 10 minutes earlier.

Anything that helps you feel better is self care.

xo, Mickeeley

DATE: _____   S M T W T F S

"Happiness is not found, it is created."
- Arnaud Desjardins

Today's Mood

😞 😣 😐 🙂 😄

Self-Care List

- .... ☐
- .... ☐
- .... ☐

I Am Grateful For

1. ....
2. ....
3. ....
4. ....
5. ....

Top 3 To Do's

- .... ☐
- .... ☐
- .... ☐

Affirmation

....
....

Inspiration

....
....

Daily Journaling Prompt

When was the last time you had a good laugh?

_____

_____

_____

_____

_____

_____

_____

_____

_____

_____

_____

_____

_____

_____

_____

_____

DATE: _____   S   M   T   W   T   F   S

"How you love yourself is how you teach others to love you."
- Rupi Kaur

Today's Mood

😦 😕 😐 🙂 😄

Self-Care List

- .... ☐
- .... ☐
- .... ☐

I Am Grateful For

1. ....
2. ....
3. ....
4. ....
5. ....

Top 3 To Do's

- .... ☐
- .... ☐
- .... ☐

Affirmation

....
....

Inspiration

....
....

Daily Journaling Prompt

What do you struggle to love most about yourself?
How can you begin to love that part of yourself?

DATE: _____   S M T W T F S

"No one can make you feel inferior
without your consent."
- Eleanor Roosevelt

Today's Mood

☹ ☹ 😐 ☺ 😄

Self-Care List

- .... ☐
- .... ☐
- .... ☐

I Am Grateful For

1. ....
2. ....
3. ....
4. ....
5. ....

Top 3 To Do's

- .... ☐
- .... ☐
- .... ☐

Affirmation

....
....

Inspiration

....
....

Daily Journaling Prompt

What emotions do you avoid? Why?
How can you begin to open up?

DATE: _____   S M T W T F S

"To fall in love with yourself is the
first secret to happiness."
- Robert Morley

Today's Mood

☹ 🙁 😐 🙂 😃

Self-Care List

- .... ☐
- .... ☐
- .... ☐

I Am Grateful For

1. ....
2. ....
3. ....
4. ....
5. ....

Top 3 To Do's

- .... ☐
- .... ☐
- .... ☐

Affirmation

....
....

Inspiration

....
....

Daily Journaling Prompt

What would your day to day life look like if you
were living in alignment with your higher self?

_____

_____

_____

_____

_____

_____

_____

_____

_____

_____

_____

_____

_____

_____

_____

DATE: _____   S M T W T F S

"Be the love you never received."
- Rune Lazuli

Today's Mood

☹ ☹ 😐 ☺ 😃

Self-Care List

- .... ☐
- .... ☐
- .... ☐

I Am Grateful For

1. ....
2. ....
3. ....
4. ....
5. ....

Top 3 To Do's

- .... ☐
- .... ☐
- .... ☐

Affirmation

....
....

Inspiration

....
....

Daily Journaling Prompt

What lights your soul up?
How can you implement that into your daily life?

DATE: _____   S M T W T F S

"You are allowed to be both a masterpiece
and work in progress."
- Sophia Bush

Today's Mood

😞 😟 😐 🙂 😃

Self-Care List

- .... ☐
- .... ☐
- .... ☐

I Am Grateful For

1. ....
2. ....
3. ....
4. ....
5. ....

Top 3 To Do's

- .... ☐
- .... ☐
- .... ☐

Affirmation

....
....

Inspiration

....
....

Daily Journaling Prompt

What bad habits do you need to work on breaking? What new habits can you adopt?

DATE: _____   S M T W T F S

"The real difficulty is to overcome how
you think about yourself."
- Maya Angelou

Today's Mood

😞 😣 😐 🙂 😄

Self-Care List

- .... ☐
- .... ☐
- .... ☐

I Am Grateful For

1. ....
2. ....
3. ....
4. ....
5. ....

Top 3 To Do's

- .... ☐
- .... ☐
- .... ☐

Affirmation

....
....

Inspiration

....
....

Daily Journaling Prompt

Show appreciation for your body. Go head to
toe and write out gratitude to her.

_____

_____

_____

_____

_____

_____

_____

_____

_____

_____

_____

_____

_____

DATE: _____   S M T W T F S

"She believed she could, so she did."
- R.S. Grey

Today's Mood

🙁 🙁 😐 🙂 😀

Self-Care List

- .... ☐
- .... ☐
- .... ☐

I Am Grateful For

1. ....
2. ....
3. ....
4. ....
5. ....

Top 3 To Do's

- .... ☐
- .... ☐
- .... ☐

Affirmation

....
....

Inspiration

....
....

Daily Journaling Prompt

If you could do anything today, what would you do?

DATE: _____   S M T W T F S

"If you're searching for that one person to change your life, look in the mirror."
- Unknown

Today's Mood

😧 😖 😐 🙂 😃

Self-Care List

- .... ☐
- .... ☐
- .... ☐

I Am Grateful For

1. ....
2. ....
3. ....
4. ....
5. ....

Top 3 To Do's

- .... ☐
- .... ☐
- .... ☐

Affirmation

....
....

Inspiration

....
....

Daily Journaling Prompt

What do you value most in relationships?

DATE: _____   S M T W T F S

"Your only limit is your mind."
- Unknown

Today's Mood

😞 😣 😐 ☺️ 😃

Self-Care List

- .... ☐
- .... ☐
- .... ☐

I Am Grateful For

1. ....
2. ....
3. ....
4. ....
5. ....

Top 3 To Do's

- .... ☐
- .... ☐
- .... ☐

Affirmation

....
....

Inspiration

....
....

Daily Journaling Prompt

How do you adapt when things don't go as planned?

_____

_____

_____

_____

_____

_____

_____

_____

_____

_____

_____

_____

_____

DATE: _____   S M T W T F S

"There is no force equal to a woman determined to rise."
- W.E.B. Dubois

Today's Mood

😞 😟 😐 🙂 😄

Self-Care List

- .... ☐
- .... ☐
- .... ☐

I Am Grateful For

1. ....
2. ....
3. ....
4. ....
5. ....

Top 3 To Do's

- .... ☐
- .... ☐
- .... ☐

Affirmation

....
....

Inspiration

....
....

Daily Journaling Prompt

Where do you want to be by this time next year?

_____

_____

_____

_____

_____

_____

_____

_____

_____

_____

_____

_____

_____

DATE: _____   S M T W T F S

"Love yourself so much that when someone treats
you wrong, you recognize it."
- Rena Rose

Today's Mood

☹ ☹ 😐 ☺ 😄

Self-Care List

- .... ☐
- .... ☐
- .... ☐

I Am Grateful For

1. ....
2. ....
3. ....
4. ....
5. ....

Top 3 To Do's

- .... ☐
- .... ☐
- .... ☐

Affirmation

....
....

Inspiration

....
....

Daily Journaling Prompt

What's on my mind right now?

DATE: _____   S M T W T F S

"Whatever you are be a good one."
- Abraham Lincoln

Today's Mood

☹ 🙁 😐 🙂 😃

Self-Care List

- .... ☐
- .... ☐
- .... ☐

I Am Grateful For

1. ....
2. ....
3. ....
4. ....
5. ....

Top 3 To Do's

- .... ☐
- .... ☐
- .... ☐

Affirmation

....
....

Inspiration

....
....

Daily Journaling Prompt

What limiting beliefs are holding you back?

DATE: _____   S M T W T F S

*"Find joy in discovering what makes
your soul happy."*
- Aly Aubrey

Today's Mood

☹ 🙁 😐 🙂 😃

Self-Care List

- .... ☐
- .... ☐
- .... ☐

I Am Grateful For

1. ....
2. ....
3. ....
4. ....
5. ....

Top 3 To Do's

- .... ☐
- .... ☐
- .... ☐

Affirmation

....
....

Inspiration

....
....

Daily Journaling Prompt

Who or what makes you the happiest?

DATE: _____ S M T W T F S

*"When the mind is pure, joy follows like
a shadow that never leaves."*
- Buddha

Today's Mood

☹ ☹ 😐 ☺ 😃

Self-Care List

- .... ☐
- .... ☐
- .... ☐

I Am Grateful For

1. ....
2. ....
3. ....
4. ....
5. ....

Top 3 To Do's

- .... ☐
- .... ☐
- .... ☐

Affirmation

....
....

Inspiration

....
....

Daily Journaling Prompt

How do you feel about the current obstacles
you're facing?

DATE: _____   S M T W T F S

"A woman is the full circle. Within her is the
power to create, nurture, and transform."
- Diane Mariechild

Today's Mood

☹ ☹ 😐 ☺ 😄

Self-Care List

- .... ☐
- .... ☐
- .... ☐

I Am Grateful For

1. ....
2. ....
3. ....
4. ....
5. ....

Top 3 To Do's

- .... ☐
- .... ☐
- .... ☐

Affirmation

....
....

Inspiration

....
....

Daily Journaling Prompt

Write a letter to your younger self and tell her
what she needs to know right now.

_____

_____

_____

_____

_____

_____

_____

_____

_____

_____

_____

_____

_____

_____

_____

DATE: _____   S M T W T F S

*"To love oneself is the beginning of
a lifelong romance."*
- Oscar Wilde

Today's Mood

☹ ☹ 😐 ☺ 😃

Self-Care List

- .... ☐
- .... ☐
- .... ☐

I Am Grateful For

1. ....
2. ....
3. ....
4. ....
5. ....

Top 3 To Do's

- .... ☐
- .... ☐
- .... ☐

Affirmation

....
....

Inspiration

....
....

Daily Journaling Prompt

How often do you practice self care?
Are you okay with that amount of time?

DATE: _____   S M T W T F S

"A flower blooms for its own joy."
- Oscar Wilde

Today's Mood

🙁 ☹️ 😐 🙂 😄

Self-Care List

- .... ☐
- .... ☐
- .... ☐

I Am Grateful For

1. ....
2. ....
3. ....
4. ....
5. ....

Top 3 To Do's

- .... ☐
- .... ☐
- .... ☐

Affirmation

....
....

Inspiration

....
....

Daily Journaling Prompt

How can you become more confident?

DATE: _____

S M T W T F S

"Choose to be happy; thats the only way to find happiness."
- Debasish Mridha

Today's Mood

☹ ☹ 😐 🙂 😃

Self-Care List

- .... ☐
- .... ☐
- .... ☐

I Am Grateful For

1. ....
2. ....
3. ....
4. ....
5. ....

Top 3 To Do's

- .... ☐
- .... ☐
- .... ☐

Affirmation

....
....

Inspiration

....
....

Daily Journaling Prompt

The hardest part about this past week was...

_____

_____

_____

_____

_____

_____

_____

_____

_____

_____

_____

_____

_____

_____

_____

DATE: _____   S M T W T F S

"Dream with ambition, lead with conviction, and see yourself in a way that others might not see you, simply because they've never seen it before. "
- Vice President Kamala Harris

Today's Mood

😣 😖 😐 ☺ 😄

Self-Care List

- .... ☐
- .... ☐
- .... ☐

I Am Grateful For

1. ....
2. ....
3. ....
4. ....
5. ....

Top 3 To Do's

- .... ☐
- .... ☐
- .... ☐

Affirmation

....
....

Inspiration

....
....

Daily Journaling Prompt

What are 10 things you are proud of yourself for?

DATE: _____ S M T W T F S

*"Today is your opportunity to build
the tomorrow you want."*
- Ken Poirot

Today's Mood

☹ ☹ 😐 ☺ 😄

Self-Care List

- .... ▢
- .... ▢
- .... ▢

I Am Grateful For

1. ....
2. ....
3. ....
4. ....
5. ....

Top 3 To Do's

- .... ▢
- .... ▢
- .... ▢

Affirmation

....
....

Inspiration

....
....

Daily Journaling Prompt

If you were able to have one superpower, what would it be? Why?

DATE: _____

"There are two ways of spreading light: to be the candle or the mirror that reflects it."
- Edith Wharton

Today's Mood

☹ ☹ 😐 🙂 😃

Self-Care List

- .... ☐
- .... ☐
- .... ☐

I Am Grateful For

1. ....
2. ....
3. ....
4. ....
5. ....

Top 3 To Do's

- .... ☐
- .... ☐
- .... ☐

Affirmation

....
....

Inspiration

....
....

Daily Journaling Prompt

How can you be a light in someone else's life
this week?

DATE: _____

*"One day you just get tired of the b*llshit
and decide to choose you."
- Mickeeley Salamanca*

Today's Mood

😞 😣 😐 🙂 😄

Self-Care List

- .... ☐
- .... ☐
- .... ☐

I Am Grateful For

1. ....
2. ....
3. ....
4. ....
5. ....

Top 3 To Do's

- .... ☐
- .... ☐
- .... ☐

Affirmation

....

....

Inspiration

....

....

Daily Journaling Prompt

How can you choose to put you first today?

DATE: _____   S M T W T F S

"The only person you are destined to become
is the person you decide to be."
- Ralph Waldo Emerson

Today's Mood

😟 😣 😐 🙂 😃

Self-Care List

- .... ☐
- .... ☐
- .... ☐

I Am Grateful For

1. ....
2. ....
3. ....
4. ....
5. ....

Top 3 To Do's

- .... ☐
- .... ☐
- .... ☐

Affirmation

....
....

Inspiration

....
....

Daily Journaling Prompt

What do you need to forgive and release?

DATE: _____   S   M   T   W   T   F   S

"The empowered woman is powerful beyond
measure and beautiful beyond description."
- Steve Maraboli

Today's Mood

☹ ☹ 😐 ☺ 😃

Self-Care List

- .... ☐
- .... ☐
- .... ☐

I Am Grateful For

1. ....,.......................
2. ....
3. ....
4. ....
5. ....

Top 3 To Do's

- .... ☐
- .... ☐
- .... ☐

Affirmation

....
....

Inspiration

....
....

Daily Journaling Prompt

How can you help support and empower
other women?

_____

_____

_____

_____

_____

_____

_____

_____

_____

_____

_____

_____

_____

DATE: _____   S M T W T F S

"Be the change you want to see in the world."
- Gandhi

Today's Mood

Self-Care List

- .... ☐
- .... ☐
- .... ☐

I Am Grateful For

1. ....
2. ....
3. ....
4. ....
5. ....

Top 3 To Do's

- .... ☐
- .... ☐
- .... ☐

Affirmation

....
....

Inspiration

....
....

Daily Journaling Prompt

If you could change one thing about the world
today, what would it be?

_____

_____

_____

_____

_____

_____

_____

_____

_____

_____

_____

_____

_____

_____

_____

_____

DATE: _____   S M T W T F S

"Women are the largest untapped reservoir
of talent in the world. "
- Hilary Clinton

Today's Mood

☹ 😦 😐 🙂 😃

Self-Care List

- .... ☐
- .... ☐
- .... ☐

I Am Grateful For

1. ....
2. ....
3. ....
4. ....
5. ....

Top 3 To Do's

- .... ☐
- .... ☐
- .... ☐

Affirmation

....
....

Inspiration

....
....

Daily Journaling Prompt

What's in your untapped reservoir? How can you
unlock that potential?

_____

_____

_____

_____

_____

_____

_____

_____

_____

_____

_____

_____

_____

_____

_____

DATE: _____   S M T W T F S

"Take responsibility of your own happiness, never
put it in other people's hands."
- Roy T Bennett

Today's Mood

☹ ☹ 😐 ☺ 😃

Self-Care List

- .... ☐
- .... ☐
- .... ☐

I Am Grateful For

1. ....
2. ....
3. ....
4. ....
5. ....

Top 3 To Do's

- .... ☐
- .... ☐
- .... ☐

Affirmation

....
....

Inspiration

....
....

Daily Journaling Prompt

Can you think of a situation you put someone else's happiness before your own? Why did you?

_____

_____

_____

_____

_____

_____

_____

_____

_____

_____

_____

_____

_____

DATE: _____   S M T W T F S

"How wonderful it is that nobody need wait a single
moment before starting to improve the world."
- Anne Frank

Today's Mood

☹ 😦 😐 🙂 😃

Self-Care List

- .... ☐
- .... ☐
- .... ☐

I Am Grateful For

1. ....
2. ....
3. ....
4. ....
5. ....

Top 3 To Do's

- .... ☐
- .... ☐
- .... ☐

Affirmation

....
....

Inspiration

....
....

Daily Journaling Prompt

What is holding you back?

DATE: _____   S M T W T F S

"You cannot find peace by avoiding life."
- Michael Cunningham

Today's Mood

😞 😟 😐 🙂 😄

Self-Care List

- .... ☐
- .... ☐
- .... ☐

I Am Grateful For

1. ....
2. ....
3. ....
4. ....
5. ....

Top 3 To Do's

- .... ☐
- .... ☐
- .... ☐

Affirmation

....
....

Inspiration

....
....

Daily Journaling Prompt

Is there a person/situation you need to resolve?
How can you do it peacefully?

_____

_____

_____

_____

_____

_____

_____

_____

_____

_____

_____

_____

_____

DATE: _____   S M T W T F S

"It is better to live your own destiny imperfectly than to live an imitation of someone else's life with perfection."
- Bagavad Gita

Today's Mood

☹ ☹ 😐 ☺ 😄

Self-Care List

- .... ☐
- .... ☐
- .... ☐

I Am Grateful For

1. ....
2. ....
3. ....
4. ....
5. ....

Top 3 To Do's

- .... ☐
- .... ☐
- .... ☐

Affirmation

....

Inspiration

....
....

Daily Journaling Prompt

Is there anything in your life you
are taking for granted?

DATE: _____   S M T W T F S

"A girl should be two things: who and what she wants."
- Coco Chanel

Today's Mood

😣 😞 😐 🙂 😄

I Am Grateful For

1. ....
2. ....
3. ....
4. ....
5. ....

Self-Care List

- .... ☐
- .... ☐
- .... ☐

Top 3 To Do's

- .... ☐
- .... ☐
- .... ☐

Affirmation

....
....

Inspiration

....
....

Daily Journaling Prompt

Who do you want to be? Are you living that way?

DATE: _____   S M T W T F S

"Don't expect to see a change if you don't make one."
- Unknown

Today's Mood

😞 😦 😐 🙂 😃

Self-Care List

- .... ☐
- .... ☐
- .... ☐

I Am Grateful For

1. ....
2. ....
3. ....
4. ....
5. ....

Top 3 To Do's

- .... ☐
- .... ☐
- .... ☐

Affirmation

....
....

Inspiration

....
....

Daily Journaling Prompt

What are 10 things that bring you joy right now?

_____

_____

_____

_____

_____

_____

_____

_____

_____

_____

_____

_____

_____

_____

_____

_____

DATE: _____   S M T W T F S

"Every moment is a fresh beginning."
- T.S. Eliot

Today's Mood

☹ 😦 😐 🙂 😄

Self-Care List

- .... ☐
- .... ☐
- .... ☐

I Am Grateful For

1. ....
2. ....
3. ....
4. ....
5. ....

Top 3 To Do's

- .... ☐
- .... ☐
- .... ☐

Affirmation

....
....

Inspiration

....
....

Daily Journaling Prompt

What area of your life need a fresh start?

_____

_____

_____

_____

_____

_____

_____

_____

_____

_____

_____

_____

_____

_____

DATE: _____   S M T W T F S

"I think that passion is the secret ingredient that drives hard work and excellence."
- Kelly Ayotte

Today's Mood

😞 😟 😐 🙂 😄

Self-Care List

- .... ☐
- .... ☐
- .... ☐

I Am Grateful For

1. ....
2. ....
3. ....
4. ....
5. ....

Top 3 To Do's

- .... ☐
- .... ☐
- .... ☐

Affirmation

....
....

Inspiration

....
....

Daily Journaling Prompt

What are you passionate about in this season of life?

_____

_____

_____

_____

_____

_____

_____

_____

_____

_____

_____

_____

_____

_____

DATE: _____   S M T W T F S

"Don't stop when you're tired. Stop when you're done."
- Wesley Snipes

Today's Mood

☹ ☹ 😐 ☺ 😃

Self-Care List

- .... ⃝
- .... ⃝
- .... ⃝

I Am Grateful For

1. ....
2. ....
3. ....
4. ....
5. ....

Top 3 To Do's

- .... ⃝
- .... ⃝
- .... ⃝

Affirmation

....
....

Inspiration

....
....

Daily Journaling Prompt

Who is your biggest role model? Why?

DATE: _____   S M T W T F S

"If you lose someone, but find yourself, you won."
- Unknown

Today's Mood

☹ ☹ 😐 ☺ 😃

Self-Care List

- .... ☐
- .... ☐
- .... ☐

I Am Grateful For

1. ....
2. ....
3. ....
4. ....
5. ....

Top 3 To Do's

- .... ☐
- .... ☐
- .... ☐

Affirmation

....
....

Inspiration

....
....

Daily Journaling Prompt

Who have you lost in life because of your choices?
Was it worth it?

DATE: _____   S M T W T F S

"You do not find the happy life. You make it."
- Camilla Eyring Kimball

Today's Mood

☹ ☹ 😐 ☺ 😃

Self-Care List

- .... ☐
- .... ☐
- .... ☐

I Am Grateful For

1. ....
2. ....
3. ....
4. ....
5. ....

Top 3 To Do's

- .... ☐
- .... ☐
- .... ☐

Affirmation

....
....

Inspiration

....
....

Daily Journaling Prompt

What would your life look like if you let
go of all the expectations?

_____

_____

_____

_____

_____

_____

_____

_____

_____

_____

_____

_____

_____

_____

DATE: _____

"Hope is the most exciting thing there is in life."
- Mandy Moore

Today's Mood

☹ ☹ 😐 🙂 😃

Self-Care List

- .... ☐
- .... ☐
- .... ☐

I Am Grateful For

1. ....
2. ....
3. ....
4. ....
5. ....

Top 3 To Do's

- .... ☐
- .... ☐
- .... ☐

Affirmation

....
....

Inspiration

....
....

Daily Journaling Prompt

What is something you are looking
forward to right now?

DATE: _____   S M T W T F S

"Life is like riding a bicycle. To keep your balance, you must keep moving."
- Albert Einstein

Today's Mood

☹ ☹ 😐 ☺ 😃

Self-Care List

- .... ☐
- .... ☐
- .... ☐

I Am Grateful For

1. ....
2. ....
3. ....
4. ....
5. ....

Top 3 To Do's

- .... ☐
- .... ☐
- .... ☐

Affirmation

....
....

Inspiration

....
....

Daily Journaling Prompt

What all are you balancing right now?
Is it all necessary or can you cut something out?

DATE: _____   S M T W T F S

"She remembered who she was and the game changed."
- Lalah Delia

Today's Mood

🙁 ☹️ 😐 🙂 😀

Self-Care List

- .... ☐
- .... ☐
- .... ☐

I Am Grateful For

1. ....
2. ....
3. ....
4. ....
5. ....

Top 3 To Do's

- .... ☐
- .... ☐
- .... ☐

Affirmation

....
....

Inspiration

....
....

Daily Journaling Prompt

What is something that use to light you up,
but you don't do anymore?

DATE: _____   S M T W T F S

"Believe you can and you're already halfway there."
- Theodore Roosevelt

Today's Mood

😞 😦 😐 🙂 😃

Self-Care List

- .... ☐
- .... ☐
- .... ☐

I Am Grateful For

1. ....
2. ....
3. ....
4. ....
5. ....

Top 3 To Do's

- .... ☐
- .... ☐
- .... ☐

Affirmation

....
....

Inspiration

....
....

Daily Journaling Prompt

Pick one limiting belief you tell yourself.
Now re-write the story into an affirmation.

DATE: _____   S M T W T F S

"Choose to be optimistic, it feels better."
- Dalai Lama

Today's Mood

😣 😕 😐 🙂 😄

Self-Care List

- .... ☐
- .... ☐
- .... ☐

I Am Grateful For

1. ....
2. ....
3. ....
4. ....
5. ....

Top 3 To Do's

- .... ☐
- .... ☐
- .... ☐

Affirmation

....
....

Inspiration

....
....

Daily Journaling Prompt

Write a letter to your future self.
What do you want her to remember or know?

DATE: _____   S M T W T F S

"You make a life out of what you have, not what you're missing."
- Kate Morton

Today's Mood

🙁 ☹️ 😐 🙂 😀

Self-Care List

- .... ☐
- .... ☐
- .... ☐

I Am Grateful For

1. ....
2. ....
3. ....
4. ....
5. ....

Top 3 To Do's

- .... ☐
- .... ☐
- .... ☐

Affirmation

....
....

Inspiration

....
....

Daily Journaling Prompt

What do you need to forgive yourself for?

DATE: _____   S M T W T F S

"The secret to our success is that
we never, never give up."
- Wilma Mankiller

Today's Mood

☹ ☹ 😐 ☺ 😄

Self-Care List

- .... ☐
- .... ☐
- .... ☐

I Am Grateful For

1. ....
2. ....
3. ....
4. ....
5. ....

Top 3 To Do's

- .... ☐
- .... ☐
- .... ☐

Affirmation

....
....

Inspiration

....
....

Daily Journaling Prompt

How do you respond to change?
Do you think you should respond differently?

_____

_____

_____

_____

_____

_____

_____

_____

_____

_____

_____

_____

_____

_____

_____

DATE: _____   S M T W T F S

"A smooth sea never made a skilled sailor."
- Franklin D Roosevelt

Today's Mood

☹ ☹ 😐 ☺ 😃

Self-Care List

- .... ☐
- .... ☐
- .... ☐

I Am Grateful For

1. ....
2. ....
3. ....
4. ....
5. ....

Top 3 To Do's

- .... ☐
- .... ☐
- .... ☐

Affirmation

....
....

Inspiration

....
....

Daily Journaling Prompt

What is one thing you are really good at?

DATE: _____   S   M   T   W   T   F   S

"The only limits you have are the limits you believe."
- Wayne Dyer

Today's Mood

😞 😟 😐 🙂 😃

Self-Care List

- .... ☐
- .... ☐
- .... ☐

I Am Grateful For

1. ....
2. ....
3. ....
4. ....
5. ....

Top 3 To Do's

- .... ☐
- .... ☐
- .... ☐

Affirmation

....
....

Inspiration

....
....

Daily Journaling Prompt

You are worthy of your dreams because...

DATE: _____   S M T W T F S

*"You are braver than you believe and stronger than you
seem, and smarter than you think."*
- A. A. Mine

Today's Mood

☹ 😦 😐 🙂 😃

Self-Care List

- .... ☐
- .... ☐
- .... ☐

I Am Grateful For

1. ....
2. ....
3. ....
4. ....
5. ....

Top 3 To Do's

- .... ☐
- .... ☐
- .... ☐

Affirmation

....
....

Inspiration

....
....

Daily Journaling Prompt

How do you define courage?
When have you been courageous?

DATE: _____   S M T W T F S

"Start where you are. Use what you have. Do what you can."
- Arthur Ashe

Today's Mood

😣 ☹️ 😐 🙂 😄

Self-Care List

- .... ☐
- .... ☐
- .... ☐

I Am Grateful For

1. ....
2. ....
3. ....
4. ....
5. ....

Top 3 To Do's

- .... ☐
- .... ☐
- .... ☐

Affirmation

....
....

Inspiration

....
....

Daily Journaling Prompt

What is one thing you can do today to
get you closer to your goals?

DATE: _____   S M T W T F S

"Empowering women is key to building
a future we want."
- Amartya Sen

Today's Mood

🙁 ☹️ 😐 🙂 😃

Self-Care List

- ....
- ....
- ....

I Am Grateful For

1. ....
2. ....
3. ....
4. ....
5. ....

Top 3 To Do's

- ....
- ....
- ....

Affirmation

....
....

Inspiration

....
....

Daily Journaling Prompt

Are you surrounding yourself with people that
inspire, empower, and uplift you?

_____

_____

_____

_____

_____

_____

_____

_____

_____

_____

_____

_____

_____

DATE: _____ S M T W T F S

"Follow your heart, listen to your inner voice, stop caring about what others think."
- Jimi Hendrix

Today's Mood

☹ ☹ 😐 🙂 😃

Self-Care List

- .... ☐
- .... ☐
- .... ☐

I Am Grateful For

1. ....
2. ....
3. ....
4. ....
5. ....

Top 3 To Do's

- .... ☐
- .... ☐
- .... ☐

Affirmation

....
....

Inspiration

....
....

Daily Journaling Prompt

What is preventing you from going after
something your heart wants?

DATE: _____   S M T W T F S

"Only surround yourself with people
who will lift you higher."
- Oprah Winfrey

Today's Mood

☹ ☹ 😐 🙂 😄

Self-Care List

- .... ☐
- .... ☐
- .... ☐

I Am Grateful For

1. ....
2. ....
3. ....
4. ....
5. ....

Top 3 To Do's

- .... ☐
- .... ☐
- .... ☐

Affirmation

....
....

Inspiration

....
....

Daily Journaling Prompt

Who is your best friend?
What drew you to them?

DATE: _____   S M T W T F S

"Just when a caterpillar thought the world was ending, it turned into a butterfly."
- Proverbs

Today's Mood

☹ ☹ 😐 ☺ 😃

Self-Care List

- .... ☐
- .... ☐
- .... ☐

I Am Grateful For

1. ....
2. ....
3. ....
4. ....
5. ....

Top 3 To Do's

- .... ☐
- .... ☐
- .... ☐

Affirmation

....
....

Inspiration

....
....

Daily Journaling Prompt

What do you want to be remember for?

DATE: _____   S M T W T F S

"Keep your face towards the sunshine and the shadows will fall behind you."
- Walt Whitman

Today's Mood

☹ ☹ 😐 ☺ 😄

Self-Care List

- .... ☐
- .... ☐
- .... ☐

I Am Grateful For

1. ....
2. ....
3. ....
4. ....
5. ....

Top 3 To Do's

- .... ☐
- .... ☐
- .... ☐

Affirmation

....
....

Inspiration

....
....

Daily Journaling Prompt

What are your goals for the next six months?

_____

_____

_____

_____

_____

_____

_____

_____

_____

_____

_____

_____

_____

_____

DATE: _____ S M T W T F S

"Don't waste a minute not being happy."
- Brooke Shields

Today's Mood

🙁 ☹️ 😐 🙂 😃

Self-Care List

- .... ☐
- .... ☐
- .... ☐

I Am Grateful For

1. ....
2. ....
3. ....
4. ....
5. ....

Top 3 To Do's

- .... ☐
- .... ☐
- .... ☐

Affirmation

....
....

Inspiration

....
....

Daily Journaling Prompt

What do you need more of in your life?

_____

_____

_____

_____

_____

_____

_____

_____

_____

_____

_____

_____

_____

DATE: _____   S M T W T F S

"Life is 10% what happens to you and
90% how you react to it."
- Charles R Swindoll

Today's Mood

☹ ☹ 😐 🙂 😃

Self-Care List

- .... ▢
- .... ▢
- .... ▢

I Am Grateful For

1. ....
2. ....
3. ....
4. ....
5. ....

Top 3 To Do's

- .... ▢
- .... ▢
- .... ▢

Affirmation

....
....

Inspiration

....
....

Daily Journaling Prompt

Do you tend to be more optimistic or
pessimistic? Are you okay with that answer?

DATE: _____

"You may not control all the events that happen to you, but you can decide not to be reduced by them."
- Maya Angelou

Today's Mood

☹ ☹ 😐 🙂 😃

Self-Care List

- .... ☐
- .... ☐
- .... ☐

I Am Grateful For

1. ....
2. ....
3. ....
4. ....
5. ....

Top 3 To Do's

- .... ☐
- .... ☐
- .... ☐

Affirmation

....
....

Inspiration

....
....

Daily Journaling Prompt

What healthy coping mechanisms
do you possess?

DATE: _____   S M T W T F S

"All dreams are within reach. All you have to do is keep reaching for them."
- Viola Davis

Today's Mood

☹ ☹ 😐 ☺ 😃

Self-Care List

- .... ☐
- .... ☐
- .... ☐

I Am Grateful For

1. ....
2. ....
3. ....
4. ....
5. ....

Top 3 To Do's

- .... ☐
- .... ☐
- .... ☐

Affirmation

....
....

Inspiration

....
....

Daily Journaling Prompt

Pick one long term goal you have and break it down into monthly and weekly goals.

_____

_____

_____

_____

_____

_____

_____

_____

_____

_____

_____

_____

_____

_____

DATE: _____   S M T W T F S

"Each morning we are born again. What we do today is what matters most."
- Buddha

Today's Mood

🙁 😣 😐 🙂 😄

Self-Care List

- .... ☐
- .... ☐
- .... ☐

I Am Grateful For

1. ....
2. ....
3. ....
4. ....
5. ....

Top 3 To Do's

- .... ☐
- .... ☐
- .... ☐

Affirmation

....
....

Inspiration

....
....

Daily Journaling Prompt

What can you add to your mornings to
enhance your day?

_____

_____

_____

_____

_____

_____

_____

_____

_____

_____

_____

_____

_____

_____

_____

DATE: _____   S M T W T F S

"Do the thing you think you cannot do."
- Eleanor Roosevelt

Today's Mood

😞 😟 😐 🙂 😃

Self-Care List

- .... ☐
- .... ☐
- .... ☐

I Am Grateful For

1. ....
2. ....
3. ....
4. ....
5. ....

Top 3 To Do's

- .... ☐
- .... ☐
- .... ☐

Affirmation

....
....

Inspiration

....
....

Daily Journaling Prompt

What boundaries do you need to set for yourself?

DATE: _____ S M T W T F S

"There is always light. If only we're brave enough to see it. If only we're brave enough to be it."
- Amanda Gorman

Today's Mood

😞 😟 😐 🙂 😃

Self-Care List

- .... ☐
- .... ☐
- .... ☐

I Am Grateful For

1. ....
2. ....
3. ....
4. ....
5. ....

Top 3 To Do's

- .... ☐
- .... ☐
- .... ☐

Affirmation

....
....

Inspiration

....
....

Daily Journaling Prompt

What values do you consider most
important in life?

DATE: _____   S M T W T F S

"Once you replace negative thoughts with positive ones,
you'll start having positive results."
- Willie Nelson

Today's Mood

☹ ☹ 😐 ☺ 😀

Self-Care List

- .... ☐
- .... ☐
- .... ☐

I Am Grateful For

1. ....
2. ....
3. ....
4. ....
5. ....

Top 3 To Do's

- .... ☐
- .... ☐
- .... ☐

Affirmation

....
....

Inspiration

....
....

Daily Journaling Prompt

What are 3 things that can instantly put you in a bad mood? What can you do to counter these effects?

DATE: _____   S M T W T F S

"Say something positive and you'll see something positive."
- Jim Thompson

Today's Mood

☹ ☹ 😐 ☺ 😄

Self-Care List

- .... ☐
- .... ☐
- .... ☐

I Am Grateful For

1. ....
2. ....
3. ....
4. ....
5. ....

Top 3 To Do's

- .... ☐
- .... ☐
- .... ☐

Affirmation

....
....

Inspiration

....
....

Daily Journaling Prompt

Write 15 things you love about yourself.

DATE: _____   S M T W T F S

"Above all, be the heroine of your story, not the victim."
- Nora Ephron

Today's Mood

☹ ☹ 😐 ☺ 😃

Self-Care List

- .... ☐
- .... ☐
- .... ☐

I Am Grateful For

1. ....
2. ....
3. ....
4. ....
5. ....

Top 3 To Do's

- .... ☐
- .... ☐
- .... ☐

Affirmation

....
....

Inspiration

....
....

Daily Journaling Prompt

What do you fear most in life?
Have your fears changed over time?

DATE: _____   S M T W T F S

"There is no limit as to what we, as women,
can accomplish."
- Michelle Obama

Today's Mood

☹ ☹ 😐 ☺ 😃

Self-Care List

- .... ☐
- .... ☐
- .... ☐

I Am Grateful For

1. ....
2. ....
3. ....
4. ....
5. ....

Top 3 To Do's

- .... ☐
- .... ☐
- .... ☐

Affirmation

....
....

Inspiration

....
....

Daily Journaling Prompt

What helps you stay motivated and focused
in hard seasons of life?

DATE: _____ S M T W T F S

"I never dreamed about success. I worked for it."
- Estee Lauder

Today's Mood

☹ 😣 😐 ☺ 😄

Self-Care List

- .... ☐
- .... ☐
- .... ☐

I Am Grateful For

1. ....
2. ....
3. ....
4. ....
5. ....

Top 3 To Do's

- .... ☐
- .... ☐
- .... ☐

Affirmation

....
....

Inspiration

....
....

Daily Journaling Prompt

What is your BIGGEST dream?
Do you believe you can achieve it?

DATE: _____   S M T W T F S

"I never dreamed about success. I worked for it."
- Estee Lauder

Today's Mood

☹ 🙁 😐 🙂 😃

Self-Care List

- .... ☐
- .... ☐
- .... ☐

I Am Grateful For

1. ....
2. ....
3. ....
4. ....
5. ....

Top 3 To Do's

- .... ☐
- .... ☐
- .... ☐

Affirmation

....
....

Inspiration

....
....

Daily Journaling Prompt

Does your work overwhelm you? Why?
Is there something you can change to help?

_____

_____

_____

_____

_____

_____

_____

_____

_____

_____

_____

_____

_____

DATE: _____ S M T W T F S

"The question isn't who's going to let me;
it's who's going to stop me."
- Ayn Rand

Today's Mood

☹ ☹ 😐 🙂 😃

Self-Care List

• .... ☐
• .... ☐
• .... ☐

I Am Grateful For

1. ....
2. ....
3. ....
4. ....
5. ....

Top 3 To Do's

• .... ☐
• .... ☐
• .... ☐

Affirmation

....
....

Inspiration

....
....

Daily Journaling Prompt

Finish the sentence:
My life would be incomplete without...

_____

_____

_____

_____

_____

_____

_____

_____

_____

_____

_____

_____

_____

DATE: _____   S M T W T F S

"If everything was perfect, you would never
learn and you would never grow."
- Beyonce

Today's Mood

😞 😦 😐 🙂 😄

Self-Care List

- .... ☐
- .... ☐
- .... ☐

I Am Grateful For

1. ....
2. ....
3. ....
4. ....
5. ....

Top 3 To Do's

- .... ☐
- .... ☐
- .... ☐

Affirmation

....
....

Inspiration

....
....

Daily Journaling Prompt

Describe a significant event that helped shape you into the person you are today.

_____

_____

_____

_____

_____

_____

_____

_____

_____

_____

_____

_____

_____

_____

_____

DATE: _____ S M T W T F S

"Act as if what you do makes a difference. It does."
- William James

Today's Mood

☹ ☹ 😐 ☺ 😄

Self-Care List

- .... ☐
- .... ☐
- .... ☐

I Am Grateful For

1. ....
2. ....
3. ....
4. ....
5. ....

Top 3 To Do's

- .... ☐
- .... ☐
- .... ☐

Affirmation

....
....

Inspiration

....
....

Daily Journaling Prompt

When was the last time you checked in with a family member or friend to be there for them?

_____

_____

_____

_____

_____

_____

_____

_____

_____

_____

_____

_____

_____

_____

DATE: _____ S M T W T F S

"I don't like to gamble, but if there's one thing I'm willing to bet on, it's myself. "
- Beyonce

Today's Mood

😟 😦 😐 🙂 😄

Self-Care List

- .... ☐
- .... ☐
- .... ☐

I Am Grateful For

1. ....
2. ....
3. ....
4. ....
5. ....

Top 3 To Do's

- .... ☐
- .... ☐
- .... ☐

Affirmation

....
....

Inspiration

....
....

Daily Journaling Prompt

What is one change you'd like to make in your life?
List 3 things you can do to accomplish it.

DATE: _____   S M T W T F S

"You never fail until you stop trying."
- Albert Einstein

Today's Mood

😠 😞 😐 🙂 😃

Self-Care List

- .... ☐
- .... ☐
- .... ☐

I Am Grateful For

1. ....
2. ....
3. ....
4. ....
5. ....

Top 3 To Do's

- .... ☐
- .... ☐
- .... ☐

Affirmation

....
....

Inspiration

....
....

Daily Journaling Prompt

What do I know to be true that I didn't
know a year ago?

DATE: _____   S M T W T F S

*"It's how you deal with failure that will determines
how you achieve success."*
- David Feherty

Today's Mood

😞 😔 😐 🙂 😄

Self-Care List

- .... ☐
- .... ☐
- .... ☐

I Am Grateful For

1. ....
2. ....
3. ....
4. ....
5. ....

Top 3 To Do's

- .... ☐
- .... ☐
- .... ☐

Affirmation

....
....

Inspiration

....
....

Daily Journaling Prompt

When do you feel the most in tune with yourself? ☾

DATE: _____   S M T W T F S

"The future belongs to those who believe in
the beauty of their dreams."
- Eleanor Roosevelt

Today's Mood

☹️ 🙁 😐 🙂 😃

Self-Care List

- .... ☐
- .... ☐
- .... ☐

I Am Grateful For

1. ....
2. ....
3. ....
4. ....
5. ....

Top 3 To Do's

- .... ☐
- .... ☐
- .... ☐

Affirmation

....
....

Inspiration

....
....

Daily Journaling Prompt

What distractions get in the way of you being more productive?

DATE: _____   S M T W T F S

"Success isn't overnight. It's when every day you get a little better than the day before. It all adds up."
- Dwayne Johnson

Today's Mood

☹ ☹ 😐 ☺ 😄

Self-Care List

- .... ☐
- .... ☐
- .... ☐

I Am Grateful For

1. ....
2. ....
3. ....
4. ....
5. ....

Top 3 To Do's

- .... ☐
- .... ☐
- .... ☐

Affirmation

....
....

Inspiration

....
....

Daily Journaling Prompt

How does every part of my body feel in this moment?

_____

_____

_____

_____

_____

_____

_____

_____

_____

_____

_____

_____

_____

_____

_____

DATE: _____   S M T W T F S

*"If you want to fly, give up everything
that weighs you down."*
- Buddha

Today's Mood

🙁 ☹️ 😐 🙂 😃

Self-Care List

- .... ☐
- .... ☐
- .... ☐

I Am Grateful For

1. ....
2. ....
3. ....
4. ....
5. ....

Top 3 To Do's

- .... ☐
- .... ☐
- .... ☐

Affirmation

....
....

Inspiration

....
....

Daily Journaling Prompt

What emotions are you holding on to?

DATE: _____   S M T W T F S

"You can't go back and change the beginning, but you can start where you are and change the ending."
- C.S. Lewis

Today's Mood

☹ 😦 😐 🙂 😄

Self-Care List

- .... ☐
- .... ☐
- .... ☐

I Am Grateful For

1. ....
2. ....
3. ....
4. ....
5. ....

Top 3 To Do's

- .... ☐
- .... ☐
- .... ☐

Affirmation

....
....

Inspiration

....
....

Daily Journaling Prompt

Write a list of everything you are worried about.
Mark out the ones you don't know are 100% true.

DATE: _____   S M T W T F S

"It's never too late to be who you want to be."
- F. Scott Fitzgerald

Today's Mood

Self-Care List

- .... ☐
- .... ☐
- .... ☐

I Am Grateful For

1. ....
2. ....
3. ....
4. ....
5. ....

Top 3 To Do's

- .... ☐
- .... ☐
- .... ☐

Affirmation

....
....

Inspiration

....
....

Daily Journaling Prompt

When you look in the mirror, what do you see?

_____

_____

_____

_____

_____

_____

_____

_____

_____

_____

_____

_____

_____

DATE: _____   S M T W T F S

"Be yourself and you can be anything."
- Katy Perry

Today's Mood

☹ ☹ 😐 🙂 😄

Self-Care List

- .... ☐
- .... ☐
- .... ☐

I Am Grateful For

1. ....
2. ....
3. ....
4. ....
5. ....

Top 3 To Do's

- .... ☐
- .... ☐
- .... ☐

Affirmation

....
....

Inspiration

....
....

Daily Journaling Prompt

Look around your room,
what items are the most "you"?

DATE: _____   S M T W T F S

"When something is important enough, you do it even if the odds aren't in your favor."
- Elon Musk

Today's Mood

☹️ 🙁 😐 🙂 😃

Self-Care List

- .... ☐
- .... ☐
- .... ☐

I Am Grateful For

1. ....
2. ....
3. ....
4. ....
5. ....

Top 3 To Do's

- .... ☐
- .... ☐
- .... ☐

Affirmation

....
....

Inspiration

....
....

Daily Journaling Prompt

Think about this past week. What did you procrastinate? How did you procrastinate?

DATE: _____   S M T W T F S

"The challenge is not to be perfect... it's to be whole."
- Jane Fonda

Today's Mood

😖 😣 😐 🙂 😃

Self-Care List

- .... ☐
- .... ☐
- .... ☐

I Am Grateful For

1. ....
2. ....
3. ....
4. ....
5. ....

Top 3 To Do's

- .... ☐
- .... ☐
- .... ☐

Affirmation

....
....

Inspiration

....
....

Daily Journaling Prompt

If you had a genie in a bottle, what would
your 3 wishes be?

DATE: _____   S M T W T F S

"Everything you want to be, you already are.
You're simply on the path to discovering it."
- Alicia Keys

Today's Mood

😖 😦 😐 🙂 😃

Self-Care List

- .... ☐
- .... ☐
- .... ☐

I Am Grateful For

1. ....
2. ....
3. ....
4. ....
5. ....

Top 3 To Do's

- .... ☐
- .... ☐
- .... ☐

Affirmation

....
....

Inspiration

....
....

Daily Journaling Prompt

What is one new thing I want to do or try this week?

_____

_____

_____

_____

_____

_____

_____

_____

_____

_____

_____

_____

_____

DATE: _____   S M T W T F S

"The secret of getting ahead is getting started."
- Sally Berger

Today's Mood

Self-Care List

- .... ☐
- .... ☐
- .... ☐

I Am Grateful For

1. ....
2. ....
3. ....
4. ....
5. ....

Top 3 To Do's

- .... ☐
- .... ☐
- .... ☐

Affirmation

....
....

Inspiration

....
....

Daily Journaling Prompt

What do I doubt the most about myself?

DATE: _____   S M T W T F S

"Never believe anyone who tells you that you don't deserve what you want."
- Taylor Swift

Today's Mood

☹️ 🙁 😐 🙂 😃

Self-Care List

- .... ☐
- .... ☐
- .... ☐

I Am Grateful For

1. ....
2. ....
3. ....
4. ....
5. ....

Top 3 To Do's

- .... ☐
- .... ☐
- .... ☐

Affirmation

....
....

Inspiration

....
....

Daily Journaling Prompt

What are 10 things you look for in new friends?
Are you/do you possess these characteristics?

DATE: _____   S M T W T F S

"When you get tired, learn to rest, not quit."
- Banksy

Today's Mood

    😄

Self-Care List

- .... ☐
- .... ☐
- .... ☐

I Am Grateful For

1. ....
2. ....
3. ....
4. ....
5. ....

Top 3 To Do's

- .... ☐
- .... ☐
- .... ☐

Affirmation

....
....

Inspiration

....
....

Daily Journaling Prompt

What can you put off until next week
to rest better this week?

DATE: _____   S M T W T F S

"It does not matter how slowly you go
as long as you do not stop."
- Confucius

Today's Mood

🙁 ☹️ 😐 🙂 😃

Self-Care List

- .... ☐
- .... ☐
- .... ☐

I Am Grateful For

1. ....
2. ....
3. ....
4. ....
5. ....

Top 3 To Do's

- .... ☐
- .... ☐
- .... ☐

Affirmation

....
....

Inspiration

....
....

Daily Journaling Prompt

What thing (relationship, project, habit, etc)
is no longer serving your highest self?

DATE: _____   S M T W T F S

"Your time is limited, so don't waste
it living someone else's life."
- Steve Jobs

Today's Mood

☹ 🙁 😐 🙂 😀

Self-Care List

- .... ☐
- .... ☐
- .... ☐

I Am Grateful For

1. ....
2. ....
3. ....
4. ....
5. ....

Top 3 To Do's

- .... ☐
- .... ☐
- .... ☐

Affirmation

....
....

Inspiration

....
....

Daily Journaling Prompt

What do you wish you didn't
have to do today or this week?

DATE: _____   S M T W T F S

"Be the change that you wish to see in the world."
- Mahatma Gandhi

Today's Mood

Self-Care List

- .... ☐
- .... ☐
- .... ☐

I Am Grateful For

1. ....
2. ....
3. ....
4. ....
5. ....

Top 3 To Do's

- .... ☐
- .... ☐
- .... ☐

Affirmation

....
....

Inspiration

....
....

Daily Journaling Prompt

What charity or organization do you resonate the most with? Why?

_____

_____

_____

_____

_____

_____

_____

_____

_____

_____

_____

_____

_____

_____

_____

_____

DATE: _____   S M T W T F S

"It's okay to struggle. It's not okay to quit."
- Gabe Grunewald

Today's Mood

I Am Grateful For

1. ....
2. ....
3. ....
4. ....
5. ....

Self-Care List

- .... ☐
- .... ☐
- .... ☐

Top 3 To Do's

- .... ☐
- .... ☐
- .... ☐

Affirmation

....
....

Inspiration

....
....

Daily Journaling Prompt

Describe a time when you quit and regretted it.

_____

_____

_____

_____

_____

_____

_____

_____

_____

_____

_____

_____

_____

_____

_____

_____

DATE: _____   S M T W T F S

*"If you want to be proud of yourself, then do t
hings in which you can take pride."*
- Karen Horney

Today's Mood

😟 😕 😐 🙂 😃

Self-Care List

- .... ☐
- .... ☐
- .... ☐

I Am Grateful For

1. ....
2. ....
3. ....
4. ....
5. ....

Top 3 To Do's

- .... ☐
- .... ☐
- .... ☐

Affirmation

....
....

Inspiration

....
....

Daily Journaling Prompt

Today I am proud of myself for...

_____

_____

_____

_____

_____

_____

_____

_____

_____

_____

_____

_____

_____

_____

_____

You did it!

You made is through this entire journal and for that, I am SO PROUD of you!

My hope is that by completing this journal, you are on the road to successfully implementing self care daily. I hope this journal has created breakthroughs for you and been a positive experience.

If you still struggle with finding self care activities to do that you enjoy, be sure to follow my instagram dedicated to self care on Instagram @SoPoshOffical.

Follow along on Instagram as well for updates on a second journal and other self care tools to help your grow your self care routine!

I hope you have an amazing day and I cannot wait to connect with you more through Instagram.

xo, Mickeeley

Made in the USA
Middletown, DE
26 October 2022

13579730R00104